AND HE SHALL REIGN FOREVER AND EVER . . . .
AND OF HIS KINGDOM THERE SHALL BE NO END

THE COMING OF THE KING

THE COMING OF THE KING

THE STORY OF THE NATIVITY

by

Norman Vincent Peale

Illustrated by William Moyers

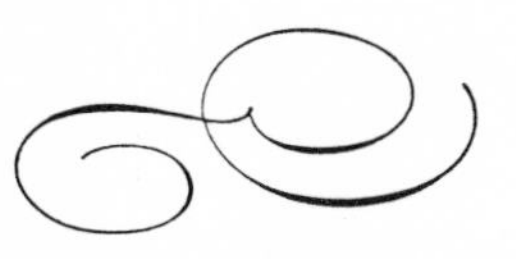

PRENTICE-HALL, INC. ENGLEWOOD CLIFFS, N. J.

PRENTICE-HALL, INC.
ENGLEWOOD CLIFFS, N. J.

LIBRARY OF CONGRESS CATALOG CARD NUMBER 56-9774

PRINTED IN THE UNITED STATES OF AMERICA

15255

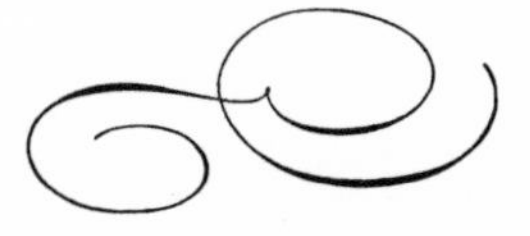

FOREWORD

"How beautiful upon the mountains are the feet of him that bringeth good tidings."

The land where Jesus walked and talked and at last gave up his earthly life for mankind still lies across the sea. How incomparably thrilling was the experience of visiting that land. How profound was the wonder of being there, of saying, "On this very ground he walked, these same hills he saw." A fresh sense of the glory and the power of his story came to me.

The country remains much as it was during the lifetime of our Lord. It is a land where white-robed shepherds still guard their flocks, where the bread is made to be broken, where nets are mended with the same motions the fishermen disciples of Jesus must have used. The sun there burns just as hotly as in the long ago and at night a sky of sudden stars moves close. It is even now practical to hollow out a cave for a dwelling rather than to build a house.

Naturally, modern transportation makes it possible to travel rapidly from place to place even in the Holy Land. The journey that Mary and Joseph and their little donkey must have found so long and wearisome is nothing at all as the road from Nazareth to Bethlehem flies back under the spinning wheels of a car. The almost seventy-mile trip, even though one ascends and descends a succession of rolling hills, today can be made in about two hours. But in this country a good many people continue to move slowly, with a wise smile for such speed. A realization that the real purpose of time is for the discernment of God grows upon one in this land.

Jesus really did come to earth to bring his tidings of peace. It was on this ground he taught, in words echoing down the ages, that the great thing is love of God and love of man. It was here that the story of the birth of Jesus came to me with increased meaning and made me want to try to share with children, by a simple telling, the inspiration of the never-old, ever-new story of the Coming of the King.

ACKNOWLEDGEMENT

I wish to offer my grateful thanks to Miss Rosalys Hall for her editorial assistance.

NORMAN VINCENT PEALE

Joseph was a carpenter. Far across the seas, in a small country at the eastern end of the Mediterranean, there is a little hill town, set among all the little hill towns of Galilee, called Nazareth. There, some two thousand years ago, Joseph had his carpenter shop in a room of his house.

They say he was a fine craftsman. Surely he was a good man and the townspeople were proud to have his work. The shop was always full of children, watching the clean shavings as they fell away from his knife, trying ringlets on their heads, absorbed in making something with the wood and the tools he let them have.

What a clean fresh smell the wood had! It was like incense.

There was an especial kindness about this man and about Mary, his wife. The children knew that Joseph and Mary enjoyed their company and their chatter, even when Joseph did not say anything, even when Mary just smiled. In the cool of the house the birds twittered softly. They seemed to repeat, "Not a sparrow shall fall, not a sparrow." The light lay golden in this place.

Mary sat more quietly now. She had always liked having the children there as much as Joseph did. These days her eyes were often upon them. Everyone knew that very soon she was to have a child of her own. As she watched these other little ones Mary pondered the glorious message of the shining angel that she should bear the Son of God.

Therefore the Lord himself shall give you a sign; Behold a virgin shall conceive and bear a son, and shall call his name Immanuel, God with us.

And the spirit of the Lord shall rest upon him, the spirit of wisdom and understanding, the spirit of counsel and might, the spirit of knowledge and of the fear of the Lord.

On a day that began like any other, the children playing outside heard the iron wheels of a Roman chariot and the beat of horses' hoofs. Up the road pounded the soldier messengers of the conqueror, Rome.

Not a boy or girl but understood the sound meant anxiety, even terror. Conquered people are always a frightened people. In those days the Romans ruled not only the Jews, but all the world they knew. Starting up and scattering like the sparrows, the children took shelter indoors with the women, while the men hurried to the market place to hear the word from their Roman ruler, Caesar Augustus.

Joseph brought back the news to Mary: a decree from Caesar that all the world should be taxed, and thereby a census taken. Each man was ordered to go to "his own town"—the town his family had come from originally.

Now both Mary and Joseph, although they were humble folk like most of the men and women on earth, were descended from Jewish families who had done great things for their people. Joseph was descended from the shepherd king, David, who slew Goliath. The city of David, Joseph's ancestral home, was Bethlehem. To Bethlehem he must go at once therefore, even though Mary was about to have a child.

It was less than seventy miles from Nazareth to Bethlehem, but Joseph was worried, as any good husband would be. The road lay through deep valleys and over mountains. The way would be dusty and difficult.

Mary prepared in untroubled quiet. She made ready her house so that she could leave it. She collected the swaddling clothes—the bands in which newborn babies were closely wrapped.

Her smile was deep. "In Bethlehem it will be then," she said.

Her good husband did what he could to make her comfortable. And all Joseph had to help him was one small donkey.

But thou, Bethlehem Ephrata, though thou be little among the thousands of Judah, yet out of thee shall he come forth unto me that is to be ruler in Israel: whose goings forth have been from of old, from everlasting.

And he shall stand and feed in the strength of the Lord, in the majesty of the name of the Lord his God; and they shall abide: for now shall he be great unto the ends of the earth.

And this man shall be the peace . . .

Morning was still far away when Joseph, taking the halter rope, led the donkey out onto the long road. Mary patted the little animal's furry neck. "You'll take me to Bethlehem, won't you?"

The heavens were full of luminous stars and in their light the carpenter and his wife glimpsed the vast procession they were joining. Many must make this journey. Mary raised her face. "The Heavens declare the glory of God." Joseph responded reverently, "And the firmament sheweth his handiwork."

Suddenly, like magic, it was full day. Hour after hour Mary and Joseph traveled on, toiling up hills, descending again. Glittering gold motes of dust boiled around them. Shimmering clouds drifted every road.

How tired and hot and gritty the people grew! How cross! Yet they thought to bring Mary water. They helped Joseph settle her when she must rest and the children plaited Mary a crown of flowers.

As they neared Bethlehem, the people began to hurry. Most of the travelers must go to the caravan shelter or inn. All hoped to reach there before the others. In pity, they were careful as they passed Mary, Joseph and the donkey, but more and more crowded by.

Joseph was so worried! The donkey's large, dark eyes fixed on those of his master. The long ears twitched forward and back. How gently he put down those dainty hoofs! Joseph urged the donkey to run.

Ah, the gates of Bethlehem at last! They came to the caves that were the inn. With all the people, guest rooms, public rooms, storerooms hummed like a beehive.

The innkeeper waved Mary and Joseph away. "There is no room for you in the inn," he called. Wearily Joseph made to turn the head of the beast. It was as he had thought.

Mary leaned toward the innkeeper. "I am to have a child."

"Lady." The innkeeper, distracted with all the things he must see to, pulled at his beard. "You have only to look. I tell you, there is no room."

"I am to have a baby this night," whispered Mary. Joseph groaned aloud.

The innkeeper was a tenderhearted man. He stood looking after them. A baby to be born, tonight in Bethlehem! Why, every cranny and corner was taken. Where could they go? There was no room anywhere! With all he had to do, the innkeeper ran down the hill after them.

He seized the halter from Joseph. "Ashamed I am to offer it—but if you can find no place else—there is the stable—among the animals. You can sleep there?"

The donkey spoke to the other animals as he entered the stable cave. Inside the cattle stirred. Otherwise there was quiet, blessed quiet. In all Bethlehem this was the place with stillness. After the heat, the nag of the dust, the thrust of the people, their own urgency, here was peace.

Mary moved slowly, very slowly, getting out the swaddling bands and the precious oil. As she had answered the angel, so now she repeated, "Behold the handmaid of the Lord, be it unto me according to thy word."

Joseph worked swiftly. With straw he prepared a bed for her. He brought food and water. He prayed. When Mary was as comfortable as he could make her, he gave the donkey hay and cool water. Joseph looked for things to do.

It was during that night and in a corner of that stable that Mary's baby was born. Because there was no other place to put him down, Joseph cleared out the cattle's eating trough and filled it with fresh straw. The infant lay in the manger. The cattle lowered their heavy heads carefully and sniffed.

Some time before, an angel had appeared to Joseph and had told him many things. Now Joseph picked up the baby and placed him in his mother's arms. "We will call the child Jesus," he said.

Bright eyes considered the baby: the donkey's, the parading pigeons', the eyes of shy things no one saw. Mary and Joseph smiled on the child. The animals' calm acceptance of life, the birds' lullabies were comforting.

And so in a humble place, even for the humble, the Son of God was born.

This holy night seemed like any other to all but a few people in the world. Who were they who were chosen to know?

Shepherds. Flocks wandered the enfolding hills, just as they had for a thousand years and would for thousands of years to come. The country where Jesus was born was suited to sheep herding and these were a pastoral people. The good shepherd must stay awake through the night. A lamb might stray away to become lost from its mother or a sheep be carried off by a shadow-slipping wolf. Simple, brave men who lived close to the earth and the simple, lovely things of earth, patient, resourceful and above all faithful, the shepherds stood for the men who followed God's will. From among them had come thinkers and prophets to whom even rulers listened. Other men wishing to lead holy lives went out to live as they did. "The Lord is my shepherd," wrote the shepherd poet who became king. Already the symbolism of the good shepherd had deep meaning in this country.

So upon the hills that night the glorious news was given to shepherds. The Saviour for whom the world had waited so long had been born in the town lying peacefully asleep near by. Could it be in little Bethlehem that this glorious thing had happened? The shepherds did not doubt it. Hearts full, rapturous, they were willing to leave their flocks, leave everything, and go at once to find him.

The scriptures tell their story.

And there were in the same country shepherds abiding in the field, keeping watch over their flock by night.

And, lo, the angel of the Lord came upon them, and the glory of the Lord shone round about them: and they were sore afraid.

And the angel said unto them, Fear not: for, behold, I bring you good tidings of great joy, which shall be to all people.

For unto you is born this day in the city of David a Saviour, which is Christ the Lord.

And this shall be a sign unto you; Ye shall find the babe wrapped in swaddling clothes, lying in a manger.

And suddenly there was with the angel a multitude of the heavenly host praising God, and saying,

Glory to God in the highest, and on earth peace, good will toward men.

And it came to pass, as the angels were gone away from them into heaven, the shepherds said one to another, Let us now go even unto Bethlehem, and see this thing which is come to pass, which the Lord hath made known unto us.

And they came with haste, and found Mary, and Joseph, and the babe lying in a manger.

And when they had seen it, they made known abroad the saying which was told them concerning this child.

And all they that heard it wondered at those things which were told them by the shepherds.

But Mary kept all these things, and pondered them in her heart.

And the shepherds returned, glorifying and praising God for all the things that they had heard and seen, as it was told unto them.

Even as the shepherds stood about the manger bed where Jesus lay, other strangers were on their way to see the baby. In the world of two thousand years ago wise men were called magi, and often because of their wisdom were made kings over their people. Far off to the East three such wise men, each in his own country, had seen a great new star blazing in the heavens. They knew from their ancient books that God had promised to send into the world a great king, who would save his people and rule over them. When suddenly the new star appeared they perceived that the time had come. They must see with their own eyes this King whom God had sent, so they might worship him.

Riding upon their camels, the magi obeyed the beckoning of the eastern star. Did one king come from Persia perhaps, one from India, one from Babylon? Crossing mountains and deserts, still guided by the heavenly lantern, their paths met at last and they came on together—to Jerusalem where the star led them.

Now when Jesus was born in Bethlehem of Judaea in the days of Herod the king, behold, there came wise men from the east to Jerusalem,

Saying, Where is he that is born King of the Jews? For we have seen his star in the east, and are come to worship him.

When Herod the king had heard these things, he was troubled, and all Jerusalem with him.

And when he had gathered all the chief priests and scribes of the people together, he demanded of them where Christ should be born.

And they said unto him, In Bethlehem of Judaea: for thus it is written by the prophet,

And thou Bethlehem, in the land of Juda, art not the least among the princes of Juda: for out of thee shall come a Governor, that shall rule my people Israel.

Then Herod, when he had privily called the wise men, enquired of them diligently what time the star appeared.

And he sent them to Bethlehem, and said, Go and search diligently for the young child; and when ye have found him, bring me word again, that I may come and worship him also.

When they had heard the king, they departed.

It was not long before the children of Bethlehem discovered the newborn baby in the stable cave. He was more fascinating to them than any toy. Shyly they moved from shadow to shadow. Inside they found Mary's wonderful smile and the kindness of Joseph who carved for them little men, sheep, goats and donkeys.

The children brought the baby gifts—a flower, some dates, a bright stone. Like all babies he curled his little fingers around theirs. Something in his look bound them to him. The children stayed to sing to him.

Outside in the streets the people crowded and jostled. Here was a shining peace, a glory and a mildness.

Had the children seen the next visitors arriving, they would have run away. The strangers came without a sound. By the time the children knew they were there, the three kings were kneeling beside them. The young ones stared at the gorgeous magi. The arms that went around the children were kind, for all the cloth-of-gold and jewels, but the wise men had eyes only for the newborn baby. Humbly the heads of these kings bent to earth as they knelt before the Lord of Lords, the King of Kings.

Three kings of the East knelt in all their glittering, glowing splendor in the hay of a stable and were proud to worship a little baby cradled in a manger. The King of Kings lay where God willed. This they knew.

The gifts the magi gave the Christ Child were of the most rare and costly kind—gifts such as only kings can offer. It is said that one brought him gold, to stand for the lovely things of the world all of us hold dear; that one gave him frankincense, a precious and wonderfully fragrant spice, perhaps to symbolize the thoughts men think; and that a third gift was a bitter gum, called myrrh, to represent the sorrows all men in this world must experience, even kings.

Lo, the star, which they saw in the east, went before them, till it came and stood over where the young child was. When they saw the star, they rejoiced with exceeding great joy.

And when they were come into the house, they saw the young child with Mary his mother, and fell down, and worshipped him: and when they had opened their treasures, they presented unto him gifts; gold, and frankincense, and myrrh.

For unto us a child is born,
Unto us a son is given:
And the government shall be upon his shoulder;
And his name shall be called
Wonderful,
Counsellor,
The mighty God,
The everlasting Father,
The Prince of Peace.